WITH JESUS
I am Talented

Copyrights

www.gnmkids.com

This book belongs to:

....

....

"Class, I have something I want to tell you," Miss Harland said. "Next week, we're going to have our class talent show."

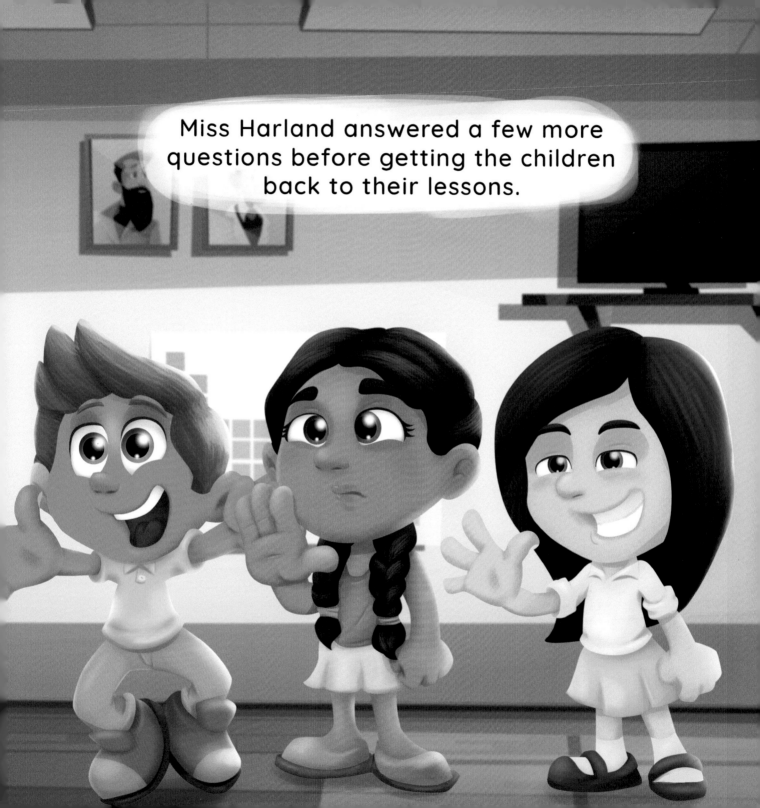

During art class, Angel had an idea. "I love to paint, so that's what I'll do. I'll show everyone some pictures I've painted," she thought.

Feeling relieved, Angel started singing softly as she began to paint.

Miss Harland heard her singing. "Angel, you sing so nicely. Will you please sing a song for the talent show?" she asked.

Angel smiled shyly and said, "Maybe."

"That's right," agreed Angel's dad. "Jesus told a story about a rich man who gave three men some money to take care of for him.

The first two used their talents to make even more money for the man. The third didn't do anything. He kept it hidden in the ground until the man came back to get it."

On the day of the talent show, Angel sang a song she sang each week at church. Everyone clapped and told her what a great singer she was.

Each of you should use whatever
gift you have received to serve
others, as faithful stewards of
God's grace in its various forms

1 Peter 4v10

Author's note:

Thank you so much for reading this book. If you enjoyed this book, we would love it if you could leave a review and recommend it to a friend.

If there is anything you would like to share with us to help us improve this book, please go to gnmkids.com/feedback

Please checkout our other books

www.gnmkids.com